FOR THE LOVE OF
HYMNS

LDS HYMN ARRANGEMENTS FOR PIANO

rebecca belliston

A Poor Wayfaring Man of Grief 14

Abide With Me; 'Tis Eventide 4

How Great Thou Art 1

Jesus, the Very Thought of Thee 11

My Country, 'Tis of Thee 21

Nearer, Dear Savior, to Thee 17

Oh, How Lovely Was the Morning 8

HOW GREAT THOU ART

Piano Solo

Traditional Swedish Folk Tune
Adapted by Stuart K. Hine

Arranged by Rebecca Belliston

ABIDE WITH ME; 'TIS EVENTIDE

Piano Solo

Harrison Millard
Arranged by Rebecca Belliston

OH, HOW LOVELY WAS THE MORNING

Also known as "Joseph Smith's First Prayer"

Piano Solo

Sylvanus Billings Pond
Arranged by Rebecca Belliston

JESUS, THE VERY THOUGHT OF THEE

Also known as "Shepherd of Souls, Refresh and Bless"

Piano Solo

John B. Dykes
Arranged by Rebecca Belliston

A POOR WAYFARING MAN OF GRIEF

Piano Solo

George Coles
Arranged by Rebecca Belliston

NEARER, DEAR SAVIOR, TO THEE

Piano Solo

William Clayson
Arranged by Rebecca Belliston

MY COUNTRY, 'TIS OF THEE

Piano Solo

Arranged by Rebecca Belliston

Small notes optional

ABOUT THE COMPOSER

Rebecca Lund Belliston has been writing songs since she was six,
teaching piano since she was sixteen, and has a song stuck in
her head at all times. A huge fan of classical, religious,
and film music, she composes mostly for piano and vocal.
In addition, Rebecca also writes romantic suspense novels.
She and her husband have five children
and live in the beautiful state of Michigan.

CONNECT :
Website: www.rebeccabelliston.com
Facebook: @rebeccalundbelliston
Instagram: @rebeccabelliston
YouTube: @rebeccabelliston
Spotify: @rebeccabelliston

REBECCA BELLISTON

Original Compositions & Arrangements | Complete listing at rebeccabelliston.com

hymns / religious

- A Poor Wayfaring Man of Grief – PS
- Abide With Me; 'Tis Eventide – PS | SSA | Inst
- Be Still, My Soul – SATB
- Come, and Be With Me/Etude in E – SATB
- Come Unto Jesus* – SATB
- Feast Upon His Word* – SSAA
- For the Beauty of the Earth/Simple Gifts – PS | VD
- For the Love of Hymns (1 & 2) – PS Albums
- How Great Thou Art – PS | VS | VD | SATB | Inst
- How Firm a Foundation/The Lord is My Shepherd – SATB
- I Believe in Christ – PD | SATB
- I Know That My Redeemer Lives/18th Variation – SATB
- I Will Make Weak Things Strong* – VS
- The Iron Rod – PS | VS
- Jesus, Once of Humble Birth Medley – PS | SATB
- Jesus, the Very Thought of Thee – PS
- Light of My Life* – Songs for a Primary Child
- Master, the Tempest is Raging – EP | PS | VS
- Moonlight Hie to Kolob – PS
- My Country, 'Tis of Thee – PS | VD | SATB
- Nearer Medley – VD
- Nearer, Dear Savior, to Thee – PS | SATB | Inst
- Oil For Your Lamps* – SSA
- Oh, How Lovely Was the Morning – PS | OPD | VS | SATB
- The Sabbath Day* – SATB
- Simply Preludes – OPS
- Souls To Save* – VS
- Still Be My Vision – VD | SSA | SATB
- Teach Me To Walk in the Light – PS | VS
- 'Tis Sweet To Sing Medley – PS | VD
- We Come Unto Thy House* – SATB
- Where Can I Turn For Peace Medley? – VD

christmas

- Breath of Heaven (Mary's Song) – PS
- Christmas Handbells for Children – Handbells
- Come, Thou Long Expected Jesus – SATB | Inst
- For the Love of Christmas – PS Album
- For There's a Savior Born* – SATB
- Hark! The Herald Angels Sing/What Child is This? – PS | VD
- In the First Light – VS
- Noel Christmas Medley – EP | PS | VD | SATB
- Come, O Come Emmanuel – EP | PS |VS
- O Holy Night – SATB| SSA
- Oh, Come, All Ye Faithful – Piano Duet | SATB
- Silent Night – VS | VD | SATB | Inst
- Star of Wonder – EP | PS | Inst
- Where Are You Christmas? – BN

contemporary / popular

- Aladdin: A Whole New World – BN
- At the Piano – PS Album
- Avatar: Bioluminescence of the Night – PS
- Batman Songs: Corynorhinus | Antrozous | Molossus | A Watchful Guardian – PS
- The Blue Planet II – PS
- Cider House Rules/Pure Michigan Theme – PS
- The Da Vinci Code: Chevaliers De Sangreal – PS
- Divergent: Faction Before Blood | Sacrifice – PS | Inst
- Game of Thrones – PS
- The Greatest Showman: A Million Dreams | Rewrite the Stars | This is Me | Tightrope – BN | EP | PS
- Harry Potter: Courtyard Apocalypse | Statues | When Ginny Kissed Harry – EP | PS
- Maleficent: Aurora in Faerieland – PS
- Memories/Canon in D – PS
- Over and Over Again – PS
- Prince of Egypt: When You Believe – PS
- Someone You Loved – PS
- Spider-Man Into the Spider-Verse: Sunflower – EP
- Spirit: Run Free – PS

classical-style

- Andante in A* – PS
- The Betrothal: Processional in E* – PS
- Come, and Be With Me/Etude in E – SATB
- Coronation: Processional in G* – PS
- Dresden: Fugue in F minor* – PD
- The Battlefield: Etude in C# minor* – PS
- Dance: Jig in F* – PS
- The Dungeon: Etude in G minor* – PS
- Etude in C* – PS
- Etude in Eb minor* – PS
- For the Love of Classical* – PS Album
- Fugue in C minor* – PS
- Heart of Red, Blood of Blue* – PS Album
- I Know That My Redeemer Lives/Rhapsody on a Theme of Paganini – SATB
- Jerusalem: Prelude in C minor* – PS
- Leuthar: Prelude in C minor* – PS
- Memories/Canon in D – PS
- Prelude in Bb minor* – PS
- Ryder: Childhood Etude in Db* – PS
- The Sea: Nocturne in D* – PS
- Sonata in A minor* – PS
- Tranquility: Prelude in Db* – PS
- Vengeance: Prelude in B minor* – PS
- The Village: Ballad in E minor* – PS

Made in United States
Troutdale, OR
10/29/2023

14123048R00018